Sticker Dolly Dressing
Sports

Illustrated by Vicky Arrowsmith
Written by Fiona Watt
Designed by Vicky Arrowsmith

Contents

The back cover folds out so you can
"park" spare stickers there while
you dress the dolls.

Gymnastics

Suzy, the coach, is helping Emily with her dismount from the beam. It comes at the end of her routine which has a mixture of balances, leaps, jumps and turns. Tasha and Chloë have been running through their floor routines which they perform to music.

Emily

Suzy

Tasha

Chloë

Surfing competition

It's a perfect day for a surfing competition. The wind is blowing off the shore, creating large waves for riding. The dolls have completed their first heats and are waiting on the beach for the results to be announced.

Georgie

Jess

Maddie

Tennis

Maria, Lily and Elena are warming up on court while they wait for their tennis coach. Today they are going to be working on their serve, backhand and cross-court techniques.

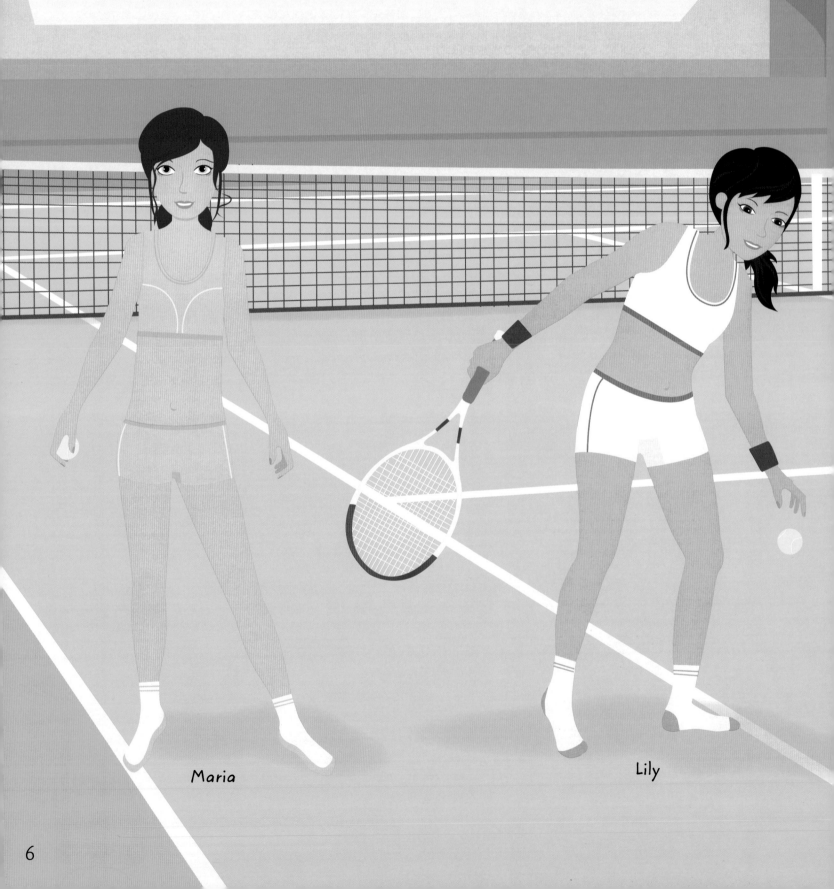

Maria

Lily

Elena

Figure skating

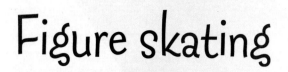

Natalie, Erin and Marta glide gracefully across the ice having just completed the freestyle section of a skating competition. Their elegant outfits made from delicate chiffon flutter as they skate.

Natalie

Erin

Figure skating

Follow the numbers to dress each doll.

① Natalie's tights

③ Sleeves

⑥ Headband

② Leotard

④ Skirt

⑤ Skates

① Marta's tights

② Leotard

③ Sleeves

① Erin's tights

② Leotard

④ Skirt

③ Skirt

④ Skates

⑤ Skates

⑥ Headdress

Page 8-9

Marta

Snowboarding

Kelly and Lindsay have had a trial run on a parallel slalom course, zigzagging side-by-side between the red and blue gates. Now it's Hannah's turn and she can't wait to try it for herself.

Kelly

Hannah

Lindsay

Athletics

The spectators are on their feet, cheering loudly, as Nicole powers across the finishing line. She raises her hands in delight as she has finished in the fastest time she has ever run - a personal best.

Kirsty

Tatiana

Nicole

Show jumping

Lauren and her horse, Lucky have just finished riding in a very tough jump-off. She is pleased that they have been awarded third place after doing a fast round and only knocking down one pole at the last fence.

Lauren

Ice hockey

The fans go wild as Hayley zooms across the rink and strikes the hard rubber puck at the goal. Jody reacts quickly and tries to block the shot with her stick, protective body padding and chunky gloves.

Jody

Hayley

Carla

Freestyle BMX

The dolls are training at a skate park. They're going to be trying out new 'air tricks' by riding the ramp, bunny hopping at the top and spinning around, before zooming down the ramp again.

Jaimie

Saskia

Beth

Swimming competition

Zoë and Abby are about to step up onto the starting blocks for the individual medley race, where they swim each length using a different stroke. The first length will be butterfly stroke.

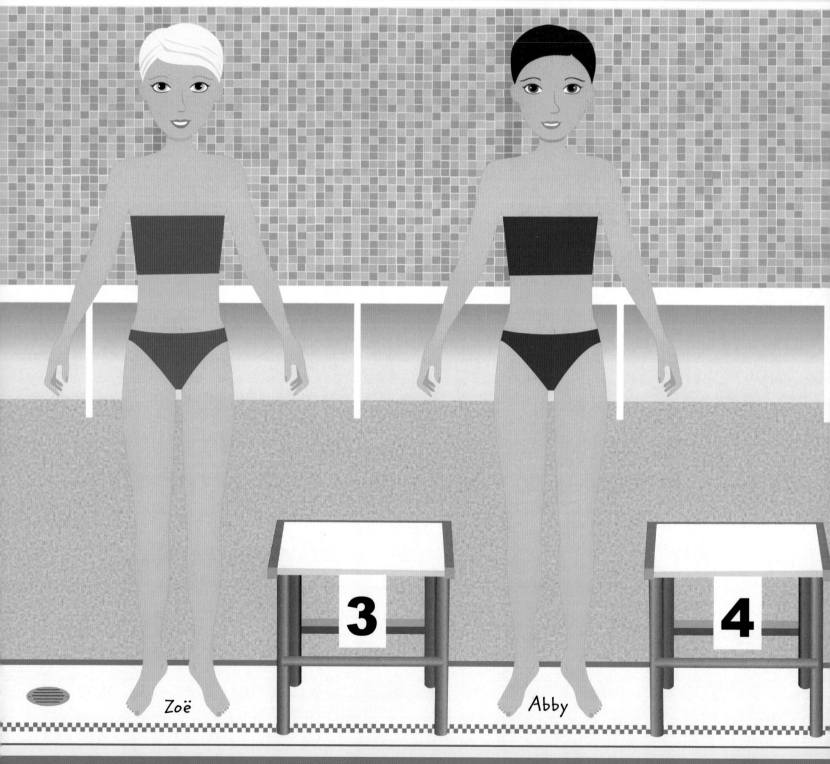

Zoë

Abby

3

4

Basketball

The people in the crowd cheer as Alyssa makes a fast break down the court with the ball. Now she's trying to dribble it around Sara who is defending her team's basket.

Alyssa

Sara

Kayaking

Wearing wetsuits and buoyancy aids, Tanya, Asha and Izzy are preparing for a kayaking trip on the river. All they need to do now is to tie their helmets securely before setting off in their kayaks.

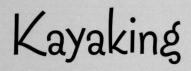

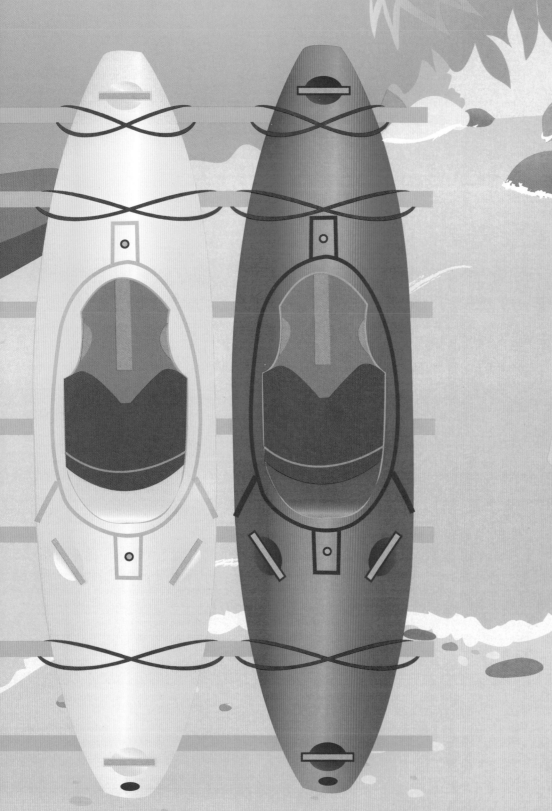

Tanya

Asha

Izzy

Taekwondo

Leanne and Mia are perfecting their kicking, striking and blocking techniques before a Taekwondo contest. Every move must be fast, precise and well-timed.

Leanne

Mia

Cycling

Rachel is having a well-earned rest after a tough climb on a twisty road race course through the mountains. Her clothes and helmet match her bike.

Rachel